Play and Learn
Spelling Book

Hello. I'm Magic Mabel and this is Walter the Wizard. Together we are going to practise spelling.

Educational adviser: Alison Shelley
Illustrator: Kate Davies
Series editor: Peter Nicholls

Published by James Galt & Co. Ltd., Sovereign House, Stockport Road, Cheadle, Cheshire, SK8 2EA, England.

Printed in China.

ISBN 0-903004-25-9

Magic Mabel's Garden Maze

Can you find the way to my house?

Use a pencil to join the letters in alphabetical order.
Say each letter sound as you go.

Start here

a
b
c
d
e
f
g
h
i
j
k
l
m
n
o
p
q
r
s
t
u
v
w
x
y
z

Use this alphabet to help you.

a b c d e f g h i j k l m n

o p q r s t u v w x y z

Find the Missing Letters

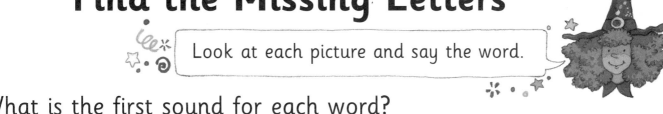

Look at each picture and say the word.

What is the first sound for each word?
Fill in the missing letters.

 gg

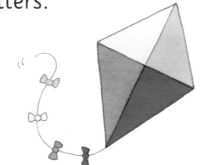 ite

 un

pple

 ig

ate

 an

oon

 ug

 at

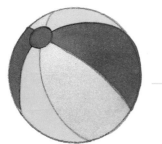 all

ap

3

Find the Missing Letters

Look at each picture and say the word.

What is the first sound for each word?
Fill in the missing letters.

oghurt

ebra

est

at

mbrella

an

og

range

ell

at

nk

og

4

Words that start with ch and sh

When c and h are put together they make the sound ch, like in the words chick and chair.

Look at Magic Mabel's shopping list. Draw a line under the words that start with ch.

Shopping List

cheese   cake

chips   chops

cherries   chocolate

Write the words for each picture.

When s and h are put together they make the sound sh, like in the words sharp and shut.

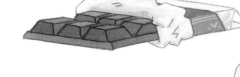

Let's make some words which start with sh. Write the word then join it to the right picture.

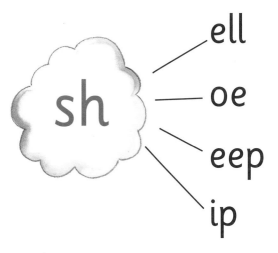

sh — ell
— oe
— eep
— ip

Words that start with th and qu

When t and h are put together they make the sound th, like in the words thin and thick.

Read these sentences and underline any th words.

"I hurt my thumb on the thorn," said Princess Mary.

King Victor sat on the throne, thinking.

Write th to make some new words.
Say each word and then copy it below.

___ at   ___ em   ___ ere

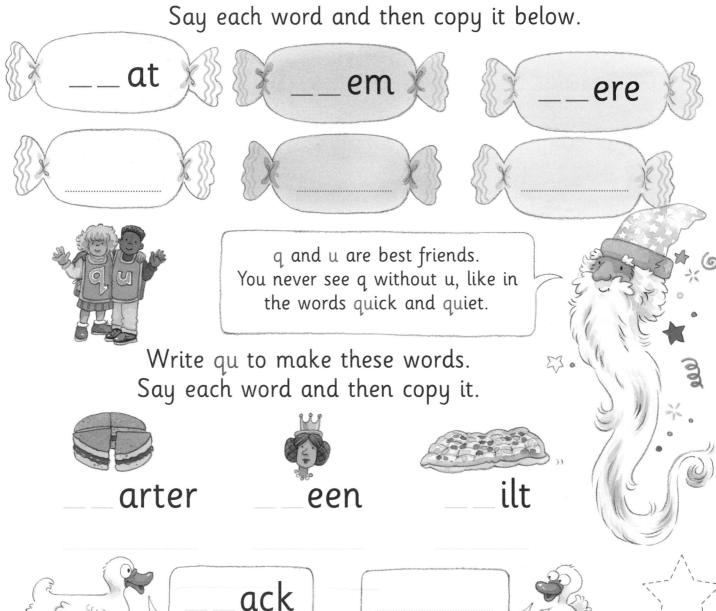

q and u are best friends.
You never see q without u, like in the words quick and quiet.

Write qu to make these words.
Say each word and then copy it.

___ arter   ___ een   ___ ilt

___ ack

6

Final Sounds

Can you find the missing letters for the words in my house?

Look at the pictures, say each word and listen to the last sound. Use these letters to finish the words.

b   d   g   m   n   p   t

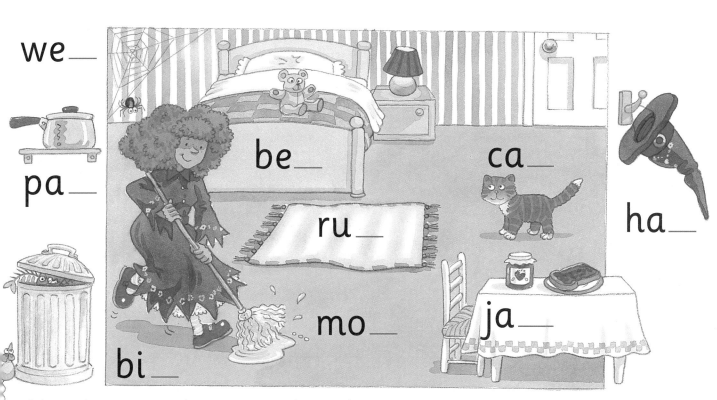

we__

pa__

bi__

be__

ru__

mo__

ca__

ja__

ha__

Use these words to complete the sentences.

 jam   web   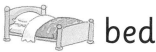 bed    hat

The _____ is on the peg.

My teddy is on the _____ .

Sammy Spider has made a _____ .

Mabel likes _____ and bread.

Short Vowels

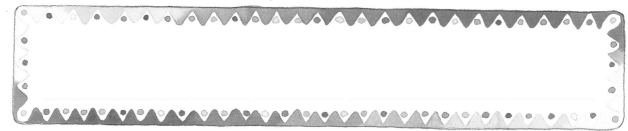

The letters **a**, **e**, **i**, **o**, **u** are called vowels. They are very important because nearly all words need **vowels**.
The other letters in the alphabet are called **consonants**.

Write your name in the frame. Draw a ring around the vowels.

Sometimes vowels have a short sound.
Say these words and listen to each vowel sound.

apple   egg   ink   orange   umbrella

Look carefully at the vowels in the middle of these words.
Say each word and write it in the correct balloon.

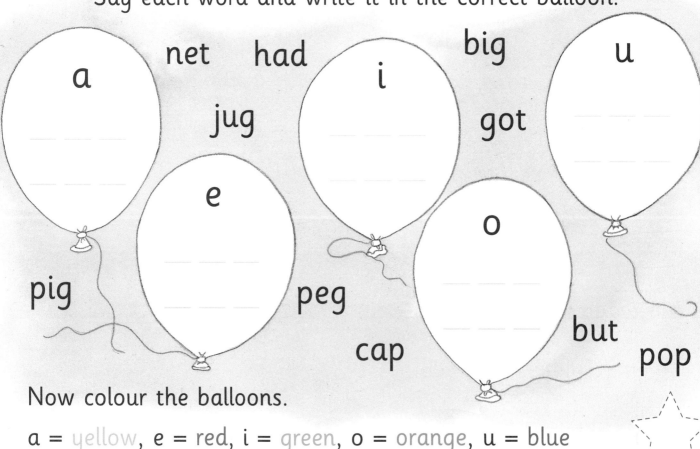

net   had   big   u

a   jug   i   got

e   o

pig   peg   cap   but   pop

Now colour the balloons.

a = yellow, e = red, i = green, o = orange, u = blue

Middle Sounds

Can you make the words by filling in the missing vowels?

a

c_t
h_s
m_t
h_d

u

s_n
c_p
b_n
b_t

o

d_g   n_t
c_t   b_x

i

b_n
h_s
p_n
d_d

e

b_d h_n

t_n p_n

Look carefully at each group of words and say the words.
Can you underline the words that rhyme in each picture?

Making Rhymes

Let's make some rhyming words. Say the words and copy them.

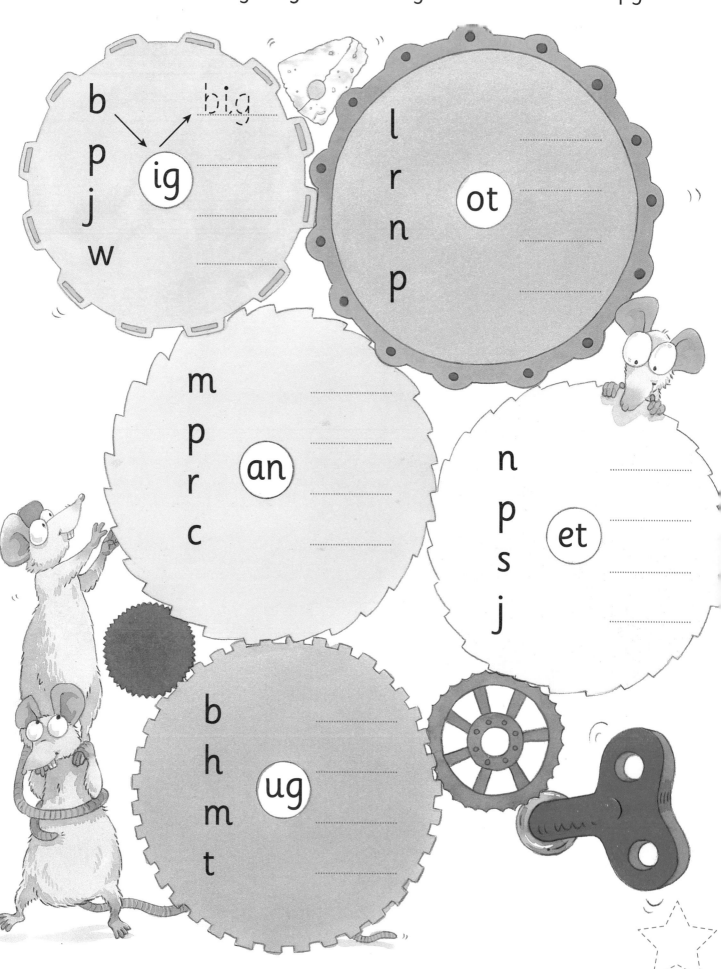

b → ig
p
j
w

big

l
r
n
p

ot

m
p
r
c

an

n
p
s
j

et

b
h
m
t

ug

Rhymes and Word Middles

Say the words in each row. Draw a ring around
the word in each row which doesn't rhyme.

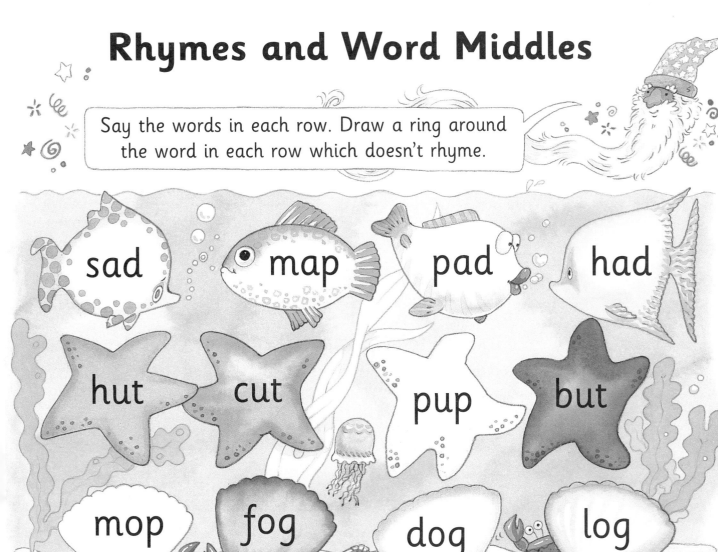

sad   map   pad   had

hut   cut   pup   but

mop   fog   dog   log

Can you fill in the missing vowels, a, e, i, o, u?
Use the pictures to help you.

j _ t   f _ x

t _ p   b _ t

j _ g   b _ s   p _ g

How to spell with Magic Mabel

Copy what I do to help you learn your spellings.

When Magic Mabel needs to learn a spell, she does it in a special way.

1. frog

First, Magic Mabel looks very carefully at the word.

2. frog

Then she says the word out loud.

3. frog

Next she covers up the word and thinks about the spelling.

4. frog

Mabel writes the word.

5. frog   frog

Mabel checks the word to see if she has spelt it correctly

This is how to spell well with Magic Mabel:

Look, say, cover, write and check.

Can you use Magic Mabel's way to practise these words? Write them on the empty toadstool.

and
said   was
who   the

Consonant Blends and Useful Spells

Magic Mabel is making some new sounds by blending some letters together.

b and l make the bl sound, like in the word blink.

We call the new sound a consonant blend.

Mabel has made lots of consonant blends.
Can you use them at the beginning of these new words?
Write each word on the dotted lines.

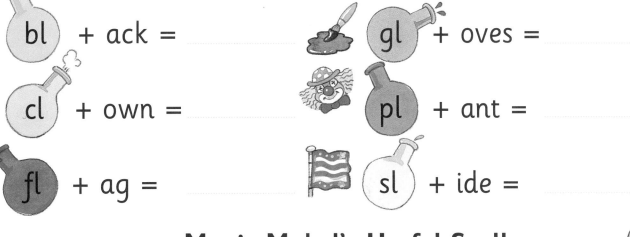

bl + ack = ...

cl + own = ...

fl + ag = ...

gl + oves = ...

pl + ant = ...

sl + ide = ...

Magic Mabel's Useful Spells

Look, say, cover, write and check.

so   some

they   then

when   where

....

....

....

More Consonant Blends and Useful Spells

Magic Mabel has made some more consonant blends to go at the start of words.

Can you find the right blend for each word?
Use the pictures to help you then write each word.

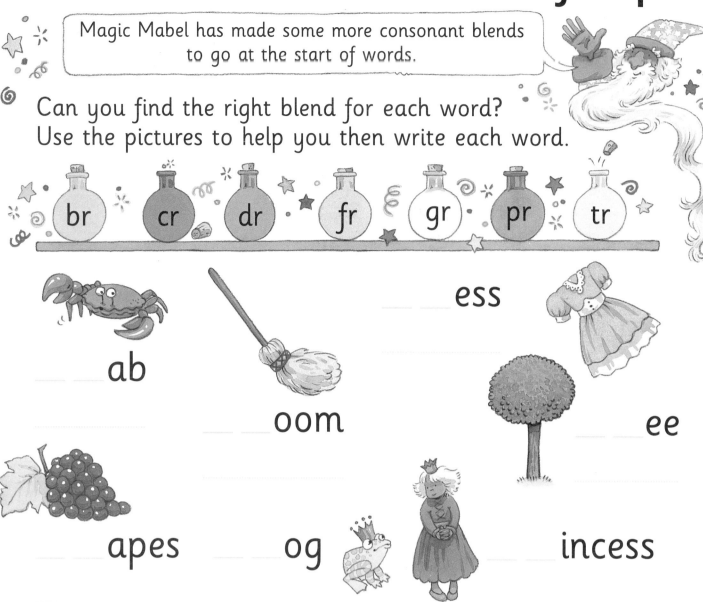

br · cr · dr · fr · gr · pr · tr

__ ab

__ oom

__ ess

__ ee

__ apes

__ og

__ incess

Magic Mabel's Useful Spells

Look, say, cover, write and check.

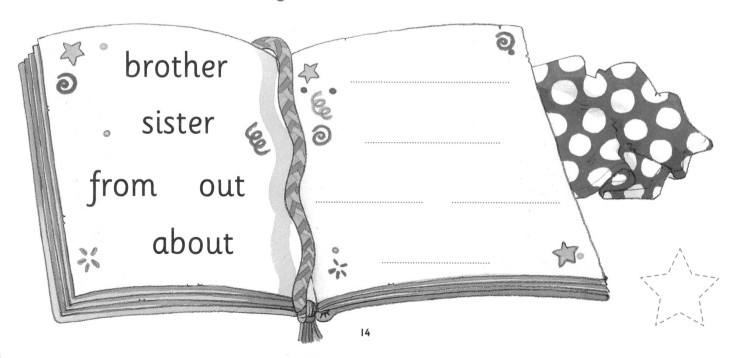

brother

sister

from   out

about

14

Number Words

| 1 one | 2 two | 3 three | 4 four | 5 five |
| 6 six | 7 seven | 8 eight | 9 nine | 10 ten |

Can you fill in the missing number words?

In Magic Mabel's garden, there are _____ flowers, _____ pumpkins and _____ snail.

How many are there?

Count each group and write the number words on the dotted lines below.

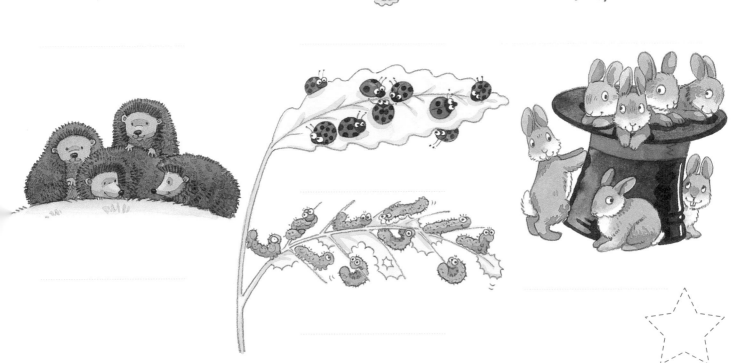

Even More Consonant Blends and Useful Spell

Magic Mabel has been busy making consonant blends which go at the beginning of words.

These blends are special because they all start with s.

sc sk sm

sn sp st sw

Find the missing blends and write them.
Say each word and then write it again.

_ _ arf

_ _ oon

_ _ ar

_ _ oke

_ _ ate

_ _ ake

_ _ an

Magic Mabel's Useful Spells
Look, say, cover, write and check.

Mum   Dad

live   went

house

Number Words

Look carefully at these number words.

Count each group and write the number words on the dotted lines.

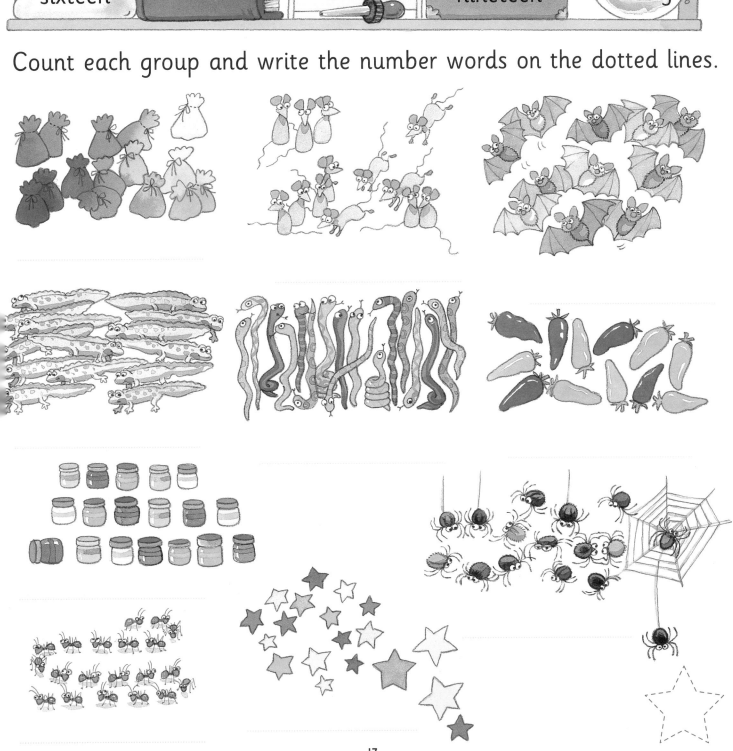

Words ending in ff, ll and ss

Some words end with the same two letters, like cuff, bill and hiss.

There are two letters but they make one sound.

Read the sentences and underline all the words ending with ff. Write the words in the scrolls.

The big, bad, gruff wolf said,
"I will huff and puff and blow the house down."
The little pig was scared stiff.
He ran off to find the other pigs.

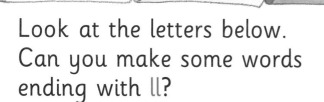

Look at the letters below.
Can you make some words ending with ll?

a + ll = ...

ba + ll = ...

wi + ll = ...

be + ll = ...

do + ll = ...

me ....   le ....

dre ....

ki ....   fu ....

Can you make some words ending with ss on the chess board?

Words ending in ck and ll

tick tock

Many words end with the letters ck. Together they make one sound like in the word clock.

It's three o'clock and time for Jack and Jill to fetch the water.

ro _ _
sa _ _
qua _ _
du_ck_
Ja_ck_

hi _ _
wa_ _
mi _ _
do_ll_
Ji_ll_

Climb the hill with Jack and Jill, making ck words and ll words as you go.

Add ll to make the words then write each word again.

a _ _ _ ....

ca _ _ ....

te _ _ ....

Say and copy these ck words.

luck   back   stick

Words ending with the consonant blend ng

I have made the consonant blend ng to go at the end of some words.

Can you use the ng blend to complete these words? Say the words and then copy them again.

ki _____   swi _____   go _____   ri _____

Can you use the words below to complete the sentences?

wing   ding   song

The children are singing a happy _____ .

My bird hurt its _____ .

The bell went _____ , dong.

Magic Mabel's Useful Spells

Look, say, cover, write and check.

just

down   little

many

Plurals

If we have more than one of something, we sometimes add an s at the end of the word. This is called a plural.

When I wave my magic wand, one duck becomes two ducks.

See if you can use Walter the Wizard's spell to turn these words into plurals.

frog

spider

cat

bat

snake

bee

Can you join each word to its plural?

tree

school

girl

boy

house

houses

schools

boys

trees

girls

Sound Matches - ai and ay

Let's look at ai and ay. They can make the same long vowel sound.

Today I am on the train.

Complete the words by adding ai then copy the finished words.

g _ _ n

t _ _ l   r _ _ l

tr _ _ n

Follow the snail's trail, filling in the missing ai letters.

tr _ _ l

ch _ _ n

s _ _ l

r _ _ n

sn _ _ l

Making ay words

s
l
h
m
w
pl

say

ay

Write an ay word on each hay bale.

Sound Matches - ea and ee

Let's look at ea and ee. They can sound the same and they make the long e vowel.

I can see a seal and an eel.

Add ea to make the words on the seal below. Then add ee to the words on the eel. Copy the finished words onto the fish.

ea

s _ _ t

m _ _ l

l _ _ f

ee

gr _ _ n

f _ _ t

str _ _ t

Magic Mabel's Useful Spells
Look, say, cover, write and check.

see

been

seen

tree

Sound Matches - ie, igh and y

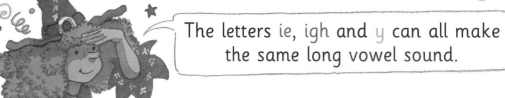

The letters ie, igh and y can all make the same long vowel sound.

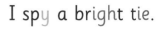

I spy a bright tie.

Words with ie

Can you make some ie words? Copy the words you make.

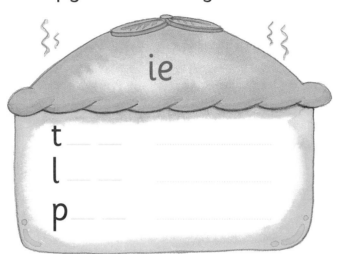

ie

t _____

l _____

p _____

Words with y

Use these y words to complete the sentences.

my   fly   by

I like _____ teddy.

The house is _____ a tree.

I can _____ a kite.

Words with igh

Put the jigsaws together and write the words.

l   igh   t   _____

n   igh   t   _____

m   igh   t   _____

s   igh   t   _____

Fill in the missing words.

I put the _____ on when it is dark.

I go to bed at _____ .

Sound Matches - oa and ow

The long vowel sound o can be made by oa and ow.

I can row my boat.

Can you use these words to complete the sentences?

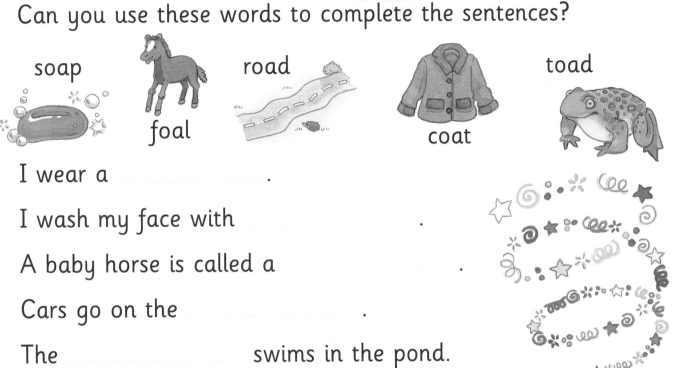

soap   road   toad

foal   coat

I wear a _____ .

I wash my face with _____ .

A baby horse is called a _____ .

Cars go on the _____ .

The _____ swims in the pond.

Let's make some new words with ow. Fill in the missing letters then copy the words onto the snowman.

l ___ ___
sl ___ ___
sn ___ ___
sh ___ ___

Sound Matches - oo, ew and ue

Let's look at oo, ew and ue.
They can all make a similar sound.

The blue rocket went zoom
as it flew to the moon.

Can you make the new words in each loop?

oo

t _____
s _____ n

ew

n _____
f _____
cr _____

ue

bl _____
gl _____
cl _____

Can you copy the words onto the correct balloons?

glue   flew   moon   true

oo

ew

ue

cool

screw

stew   pool   blue

Colour Words

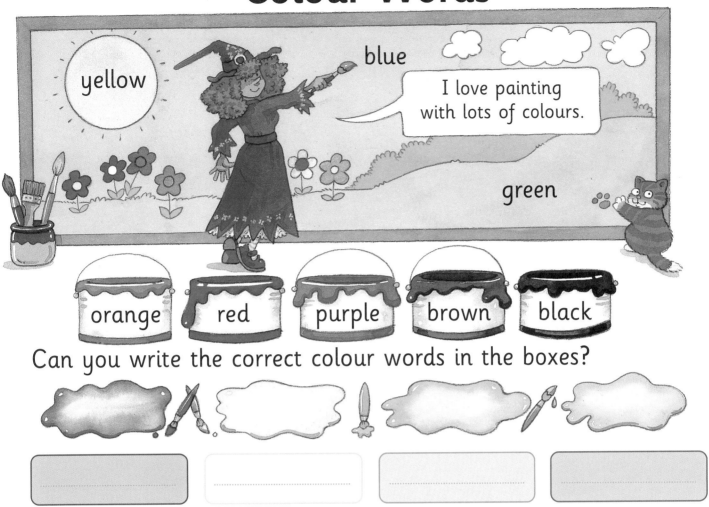

Can you write the correct colour words in the boxes?

Look carefully at the wordsearch. See if you can find these colour words: red, orange, green, blue, brown, black, purple.

y	h	o	h	e	c	h	g	s	a
e	k	b	l	u	e	z	r	t	o
l	c	t	p	a	r	l	e	h	r
l	b	r	o	w	n	f	e	r	a
o	e	k	l	s	c	r	n	g	n
w	p	u	r	p	l	e	m	s	g
n	o	r	d	d	z	y	r	r	e
h	b	c	r	m	n	p	d	e	p
b	l	a	c	k	r	t	t	d	g

Colour in the words with your crayons.

Magic e Words

If magic e is added to some words, the short vowel like a in cap becomes a long vowel like a in cape.

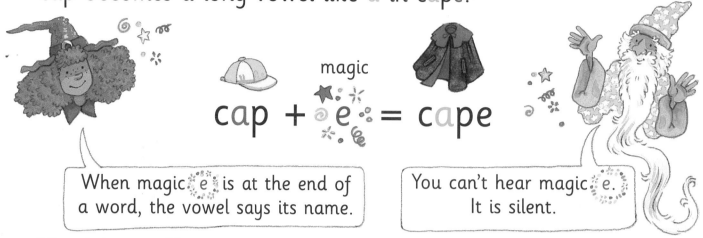

magic

cap + e = cape

When magic e is at the end of a word, the vowel says its name.

You can't hear magic e. It is silent.

The Magic e Machine makes new words by adding e. Write the new words in the correct shapes. Then say each word.

tap

mat

cub

in   The Magic e Machine   out

pin

man

cube

Magic Mabel's Useful Spells
Look, say, cover, write and check.

came
made

make
name

Magic e Words

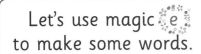

Let's use magic e to make some words.

Write the new word then join it to the correct picture.

bik + e =

tub + e =

mol + e =

cak + e =

rob + e =

Magic Mabel's Useful Spells
Look, say, cover, write and check.

like

home   time

five   nine

....

....

....

29

Days of the Week

Monday	Tuesday	Wednesday	Thursday

Friday	Saturday	Sunday

Look carefully at Magic Mabel's calendar. Read the clues and fill in the missing days. When you have done that you can do the crossword.

Across Clues

1. Spell-making day is on _____.
2. Mabel rides her bike on _____.
3. On _____ Mabel visits Walter the Wizard.
4. _____ is swimming day.

Down Clues

1. On _____ Mabel goes skating.
2. _____ is baking day.
3. Mabel flies on her broomstick on _____.

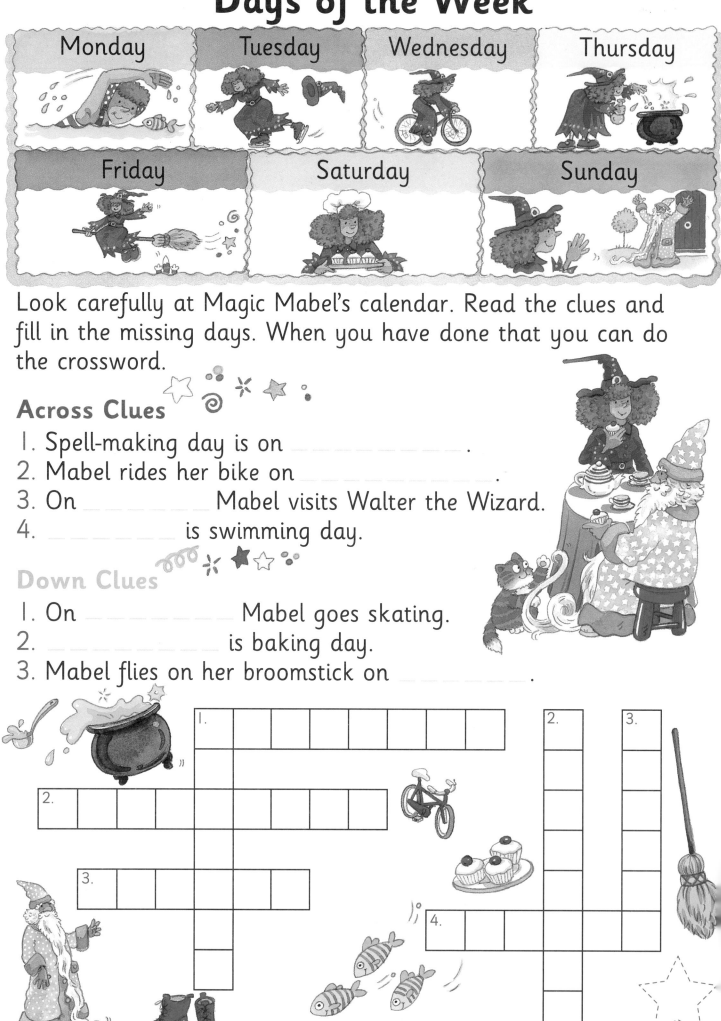

Magic Mabel's Award

is a

1 = s

4 = e

2 = u

5 = r

3 = p

6 = l

1 2 3 4 5   1 3 4 6 6 4 5

Well Done!

Signed   Magic Mabel

Magic Mabel has given you this award for all your hard work.
Fill in your name.
Solve the code by using the stars to find the letters.
Give yourself the special star sticker.

Play and Learn

Spelling Book

Answers

Page 3
egg, kite, apple, sun, pig, gate, van, moon, jug, hat, ball, tap.

Page 4
yoghurt, zebra, nest, cat, umbrella, dog, fan, orange, well, rat, ink, log.

Page 5
cheese, chips, cherries, chops, chocolate.
cherries, cheese, chocolate.
shell, shoe, sheep, ship.

Page 6
thumb, the, thorn; the, throne, thinking.
that, them, there.
quarter, queen, quilt, quack.

Page 7
web, pan, bed, cat, rug, hat, bin, mop, jam.
hat, bed, web, jam.

Page 8
(a) had, cap (e) net, peg (i) big, pig (o) got, pop
(u) jug, but.

Page 9
(a) cat, has, mat, had (u) sun, cup, bun, but
(o) dog, not, cot, box (i) bin, his, pin, did
(e) bed, hen, ten, pen.

Page 10
big, pig, jig, wig; lot, rot, not, pot; man, pan, ran, can; net, pet, set, jet; bug, hug, mug, tug.

Page 11
map, pup, mop.
jet, fox, tap, bat, jug, bus, pig.

Page 13
black, gloves, clown, plant, flag, slide.

Page 14
crab, dress, broom, tree, grapes, frog, princess.

Page 15
five flowers, two pumpkins, one snail.
six bees, three butterflies, eight birds,
four hedgehogs, nine ladybirds,
ten caterpillars, seven rabbits.

Page 16
scarf, spoon, star, smoke, skate, snake, swan.

Page 17
fifteen magic bags, thirteen mice,
eleven bats, fourteen newts, seventeen snakes,
twelve chilli peppers, eighteen slime jars,
twenty ants, nineteen stars, sixteen spiders.

Page 18
gruff, huff, puff, stiff, off.
all, ball, will, bell, doll.
mess, less, dress, kiss, fuss.

Page 19
Jack, duck, quack, sack, rock.
Jill, doll, mill, wall, hill.
all, call, tell.

Page 20
king, swing, gong, ring.
song, wing, ding.

Page 21
frogs, spiders, cats, bats, snakes, bees.